THE
*N*OTES
THEY
PLAYED

THE
NOTES
THEY
PLAYED

JOIYA MORRISON-EFEMINI

 PARADIGM HOUSE

THE NOTES THEY PLAYED

Request for information on this title should be addressed to

Joiya Morrison-Efemini
Marietta GA, USA
Email: joiyae.me@joiyamewrites.com
www.joiyamewrites.com

Library of Congress Cataloging-in-Publication Data

Joiya Morrison-Efemini
THE NOTES THEY PLAYED
ISBN-13: 978-1-946530-11-0 (Paperback)
ISBN-10: 1-946530-11-5 (Paperback)
1. Fiction - General - Short Stories - Novel In Verse 1. Title
Library of Congress Control Number: 2017952366

Cover design by Rick Olsen
Edited by Winnie Aduayi and Oscar Brent

Published in Dallas Texas by Paradigm House. A registered trademark of Paradigm Concept llc. www.pphworld.com info@pphworld.com

Printed in the United States of America.

This book is dedicated to my Dad, Andrew Morrison, who loves the beautifully written word, and introduced it to me, in every form, and with such fervor that I had no choice but to fall in love too.

And always, to my children who were all born with such pluck, and so infected me!

Acknowledgement

I owe all to my Heavenly Father, who gave His only Son, Jesus; who left for me a Comforter. Until He returns.

I would like to thank my editor, Winnie, who is as stubborn as I am, and who worked the miracle of coaxing me into turning a scrawny stab at a children's book into a robust piece of music.

To my Love, Efe. Your faith in me has never faltered. Thank you.

Contents

THE PIANO

I stand in the dark, forgotten
corner of an unused room,
left with only memories of touch.
My composition muffled,
my only purpose - the ability to
serenade hearts,
make feet rap,
and coax fingers to
scale octaves like mountains,
now lost in the
space unconsidered.
My ambition... *silenced.*

I AM THE PIANO

Vibrant!
Powerful!
Significant!
I have been moved from
and into countless homes,
from a faraway country,
across State lines,
and down just a couple of blocks.

I've been welcomed
by heavy feet and awkward fingers,
pushing and pecking at my keys.
So many players.
Such meager talent;
which is not a complaint.
For all music mirror the
essence of souls, and
I have been familiar with
such beautiful souls.

But there was a virtuoso, Helene.
Oh that every piano could
have just one...

Today, only the cat.
Aaah...the cat.

She nudges against my leg
to scratch her chin as
she saunters by.

Less often,
when the sun pours in just right,
the cat jumps on the bench,
hoists herself up and
perches on my lid,
as she bathes in the light.
She grazes several keys
on her way up between
my bench and my lid.

A curt, rude noise!
Too short and only accidental.
She will lick herself lazily.
Her purrs just strong enough
for tiny vibrations,
reminding me of being played.

Then the cat lies down,
falls asleep, and
the purring slowly
softens to a stop... *Calando*
               -(becoming softer and slower)

But only yesterday,
Helene, my player.
She had handled me the way
she had raised the children
and run the house.

> With *Brio. Con Fuoco. Dolce. Giocoso.*
> *-(energy. With fire. Sweetly. Humorously)*
>
> She had been a *Fantasia!*
> *-(not limited to conventional)*

The children had all been
happy and healthy and loved.
They all learned to play,
each at their own tempo;
some better than others.

Never as perfectly as
their mother, Helene.
But the entire house had
played in *allegro*
> *-(quick, lively, bright)*

Her man, Preston,
had never played
but had always
talked and laughed
and danced in perfect harmony
with Helene.

The lyrical magic
I have mixed through homes -
Laughter.
       Health.
          Harmony.

Now,
yet upright, I sag
in the mournful inaction of
my hammers and strings… *Morendo*
               -(dying away)

Waiting for a cat to
tread on my keys…
…to purr a little.

Helene has been gone
for many years.
Preston walks by,
day after day scarcely noticing
the shroud of dust that
now coats my clavier.

The children,
Nicolette and Annalise,
who no longer live in the house
Still come back.
They fuss over their father,

pecking and patting him.
They bring their children,
Who are forbidden from
giving me so much as a tickle.

"Old and Fragile!"
They are warned.

The shrieks and giggles of
these grandchildren not close enough.
Their pitter-patter and stomps
not strong enough
from so far away.

They all sit around
the Dining room table,
older than me,
and clink glasses,
and lift forks to mouths
in perpetual motion.

They laugh,
and sometimes cry in
remembrance of Helene, my virtuoso.
They scrape chairs across floors,
their ensemble incomplete.

They clear the table as painstakingly
as they cleaned their plates and
wash the dishes.
They handle her fragile china
with such care but...
                    Never handle me.

I'm left with only
echoes of key strokes.
Inefficacy.
All of life's lyrics left a cappella

Subito!
   -(suddenly)
A new woman arrives,
her voice *arioso*
              -(expressive, lyric)
She sits at my bench,
lifts her hands,
begins a *cadenza.*
              -(improvised, free rhythmic style).
At once peculiar and familiar.
She manipulates every single key.
At the end, a fermata.

Still, too soon
the percussion ends and

the woman's voice trails away.
Melancholy and *traumerisch*
          -(dreamy)

        I wonder...
        Was it just an audition?

In my reverie,
Or could it be real?
Recognizable reverberation from
the past visits me.
Another time,
in an unrelated home,
and long before Helene...

They are seated on
the bench together;
the Grandmother, Ola,
and the grandchild, Joy.
Her favorite.
They are all her favorite.
But this one has the gift that
Ola's mother, Mae, had,
and often reminds her

15

of her childhood.
Ola instructs Joy the
way Mae instructed her:

> *"Back straight,*
> *fingers curved like so...*
> *like my pin cushion is resting*
> *up here under your palms,*
> *with the pins poking out*
> *the wrong way.*
> *Don't look down*
> *You can see where they need to land.*
> *The music will show you.*
> *Don't take your eyes off the music,*
> *it's the map for where*
> *those fingers need to travel.*
> *Follow the music.*
> *Trust it to take you there!"*

Then the cramps come on hard
to disrupt the lesson.
Before Ola can say,
'the lesson must be over for now'
Joy stands up
and moves to the armchair.

She knows the hands so well;

16

She can see how stiff they go
when the pain comes.
She can see the ache in Ola's eyes.

She waits for her grandmother to sit first.
They can share the giant armchair,
sitting side by side to tell stories,
because the armchair is huge
and Ola seems so incredibly small.

Joy loves the stories.
She sits still through them
and sighs at all the right parts.
Her breath matching the
rhythm of the lines.

"Every person has a song…"
Ola always begins here.

*"We go through life and hit the notes
the Good Lord has written for us.
Not all of them;
we stray, of course.
Sometimes,
we play dark and dreary tunes.
But if we stop to*

listen to His melody,
we can always find
our way back."

"The things we love have songs too;
Songs we give them,
because they don't have free will,
like God gave us.
We make them play along.
That piano you love so much
was my Mother's.
Her name was Mae.
It has a song so rich,
you can feel it when you play.
I know you can,
I can see the song in your eyes,
I can hear it in every note.
Sometimes you don't know
what you're playing...
– the song on the page,
or that piano's song.
The one passed down
to your heart."

"Long ago,
before you and
before your Mama,

18

my mother found that piano
hidden away in an old house
in a dark forgotten corner
of an unused room
with only memories of touch".

This last part of the story,
"...with only memories of touch"
repeats...
for such is my state today.
Ola often said it with a
sigh so deep it hummed,
and with her head bowed
in recollection.

Lifetimes later,
Helene, a grandmother
gone too soon for
her grandchildren to recall
and too soon to
teach them that I am
Neither delicate, nor old.

I am everlasting

I am feathery, yes;
but also robust.
I am my sound -
Eternally instrumental
in fielding emotion...
in mellowing life.

When the memories in a
house become more dynamic
than the life lived there,
and none of the children sensibly
measure my value,
I am sold...
for almost nothing!

Yet, a stranger is
willing to pay mightily for
my promise, and perhaps,
deliver one in return -
to recognize me?

Suddenly,
That *arioso* voice again!
                    "Remember it?
                    ...Expressive and lyric."

I'm being moved...
        out of the corner
                out of the room
                        out of the house.

Into the cold
        onto a truck
                out of the truck
                        out of the cold.

Into a new house
        into a new room!
                And into the middle of that room!

All at once,
there is action!
New children dance about and cheer.
Warm sun pours
through the windows.
The new woman, Zara,
uses a damp rag to
wipe away my dust,
cool, yet *con calore*
      -(with warmth)

All day the children
peck and drum,
and crash on my keys.
They stomp on my pedals.

21

It's electric!
The hammers and strings
fly and flutter!

As the sun fades,
the house moves into *decrescendo*
          –(gradually getting quieter)
The children are shuffled away
I am left alone.

When all is *tranquillo*
          –(quiet, calm)
Zara returns and
sits on my bench.
She closes her eyes
and her fingers skip across
the keyboard – tentatively.
Pianissimo
          –(very soft)
Then, *fiero!*
          –(bold)
Accelerado!
          –(gradually increasing in tempo)

Though what is happening
is exactly what I was made for,
it feels absolutely extraordinary!
Forte! Presto!
          –(Strongly! Very fast!)

Zara's eyes never open.
Her man, Harper,
enters the room smiling.
He walks to us and
sits next to her on our bench.
His smile spreads over to her face.
Her fingers never falter.
He puts an arm around her waist.
She angles her head to
meet his shoulder. *Affetuoso*
                    -(affectionate, tender)

Much later,
all, but one are still.
The new cat scampers about,
fearless and *animato*.
                    -(animated, spirited)
Still just a kitten,
and cannot jump onto
my bench yet.
But I remember that
kittens grow into cats that
leap and perch,
and bask in bright rooms,
purring and reviving me
when no one else will;
when I have been long forgotten
and clothed in dust.

Poco a Poco
    -(Little by little)
the cat and I
will become grand old friends;
Both loved. Both *comodo*
           -(comfortable/easy)

For now I stand, *larghetto*
        -(dignified)
in the middle of a dark room,
in a house full of promising fingers.
Promising fingers playing in
       Laughter
        Health
          Love
            Joy...
But also in mourning
      Illness
        Resentment
          Fear...

And I...
I'm the Piano –
Present.

I soothe wailing babies to sleep;
mend broken hearts back to beating;
comfort weeping souls in mourning;

I divert fear from the diseased.

Generation after generation
I stand with my players –
Accessible.
As they bury children
or as lovers' passion fizzles.
As they pray for God to intervene
with miraculous encores as
opposed to natural finales.
When they are terrified.
When there is nothing left to do
But pray and wait.

They play me with purpose.
In rigid staccato,
Restless minds get lost in
meandering medleys;
in whimsical waltzes.
Tears dampen the notes of
continuous cadences.

Euthanasia in elegy.
A disturbing dissonance.

By rote they recite their blues

Helpless refrains follow these players
to hospitals and courtrooms;
to schools and workplaces;
to churches and cemeteries…
My tones give voice to
their sharp torments and
flattened expectations.

In these refrains, though,
The past rebounds…

    That
        Pain
           Death
              Regret
                Fear
                  Hate
                      and
                  Love
              Health
        Laughter
      Hope
  Joy…

Every affection,
every affliction,
Played with the same 88 notes.

And so these players,
do not ever forget,
even in their anguish
that the music changes,
even when the notes cannot.

And eventually,
with some guilt,
and much resistance
It does.

Such was the case
with the little girl, Joy,
who became a young woman;
and the grandmother, Ola,
who had cramped hands
that eventually became so
crinkled and set they could
never play again.

But Joy could play exceptionally
and her notes became the balm
that allowed Ola to
Endure.
And then, to let go
one cloudy afternoon in
her own bedroom

in her own house,
listening to her own music
played by her most loyal pupil,
as she went to her Precious Lord.

That same music,
granted by that same Lord,
assuaged the pain of loss for Joy,
who had honestly believed
her grandmother would live forever,
or at least long enough
to nestle her own children
in that tiny lap.

She had been too young to
weigh in when Ola died.
So I was sold by her mother
and the other siblings,
because there was no place
for me in their homes.

Years later,
after she pursued me
and brought me back,
Joy had her first baby, Andrew,
who was always most soothed
when rocked by his father, also Andrew,

in the piano room
while Joy played the songs
so beloved by his great-grandmother.

Then Joy knew
that Ola did indeed
live forever...
like music,
like Love,
like me,
The Piano!

OUR
DROWNING GENE

To granddad it all
felt unremitting;
the inevitable,
nightmarish death of
three generations –
Past, Present, and Future.
First grandma and Uncle Leonard,
and then Mother,
24 years later.

Blame could be squarely placed.
It had come as certain
as sharks to blood;
he had known it would

and hadn't filled the lake in.

Everyone knew
that my mother lived
on her own terms.
To prove a point,
she'd even died
on her own terms.

My mother...
reigned supreme,
demanding we all fall in line.
She consumed a
gluttonous host of desires,
yet, never sated.

22 years ago,
one evening after dinner,
mother, only 15,
casually announced
to her father that
he would be a grandfather.
Granddad must have been
relieved there would be someone else
to buffer the enormity of her.
And maybe someone to
finally teach her about

31

selflessness,
Sacrifice,
True love…

However,
after my birth,
mother's needs doubled;
she reigned even more.
Her majesty was something
to worship,
to pour into.
Unabashedly,
she defined herself as
'ALL'.

As a child,
I believed life was
mother above all else.
Life started and
stopped at her whim.
Surrounded by
marble,
crystal,
and Gold,
mother and I played house on
grandad's infinite dime.
In her childhood,

mother prevailed as the
'model spoiled only child'.
Her childish desires
pounced from head to lips to
my grandparents' ears,
and materialized
from heavy hearts.

After Mother,
my grandparents
had conceived other babies
that never turned up.
When they finally adopted
Uncle Leonard,
mother's selfishness was
deeply rooted in the soil that
nourished their family tree;
it diseased every branch.
By then,
her branch was much
too thick to prune.

I lived the way
mother had lived,
and I was expected to
live that way until
the day I die…

just the way she died too.

Mother told me that
grandma and Uncle Leonard
went away when she was only 10,
because they could not stand
granddad's love for her.

> *"One day they went*
> *out for a drive and*
> *never came back home".*
> She'd said.

My mother...
thoughts of her
embedded deeply;
submerged in confusion;
her hands most of all,
haunt me.

Each night I lay down
and close my eyes,
there they are...
ready to grab me,
to pull me under
to the depths they are
reaching from.
My heart races,

as I try to convince myself,

"They are beautiful.
They are tender.
They would never hurt me."

Yet,
I always wake up
soaked.

Mother's hands...
smooth,
dainty,
honey brown,
and strong.
Her touch...
like a bolt of fine silk,
sleek and polished,
but with firm support...
hard almost.

I loved her touch,
I felt it so much,
I never had to want for it,
which is why the
dreams baffled me,
until I stumbled upon
the documentary that
helped me figure it out.

35

The documentary
chronicled a family,
otherwise normal,
possessed by a certain gene:
a deafening gene
that caused half the entire line
to be completely deaf by the
time they reached their twenties.
They were all born hearing,
but something in their
genetic make-up caused 50% of
them to lose their hearing.

Deliberate drowning
is not genetic;
it's not passed down
from generation
to generation,
like that deafening gene.
It is not contagious.
It has nothing to do
with lifestyle.
It's not an act of laziness.
It takes BOTH
a 'Vibrant Will'
and a 'Dead Spirit'.

Mother...
mothered the way
she'd always been mothered...
indulgently.
Only she'd directed it oppositely;
grandma indulged,
mother indulged;
they both indulged mother.

Every decision
mother ever made
regarding me
was for her own benefit!

She'd check me out of school
in the middle of the day for
no other reason than to
see some movie that
had been out for weeks.
We'd sit side by side in
an empty theater and
pretend to be sisters.
We pretended we
owned the theater,
or were rich enough
to rent the whole place.

Technically,
we could have.
Granddad gave generously,
and we lived lavishly.
Mother was never expected
to do anything except
'survive'.

Grandad's fear that
he would outlive her
was palpable, and that was
her control over him.

For five years
she'd longed to
teach her dead mother
a lesson...
To show her that
she was worth staying for.
She'd show her by raising me,
and by becoming sustenance to me.

"hmmm...Children are
the best judges of character..."
She'd sigh every time
I told her I loved her.

38

While my friends wished
they had a mother like mine,
who didn't take life seriously,
I secretly wished for
perfect attendance in school;
a library full of books to
read out back in the hammock,
for hours alone;
a celebration honoring
my straight A's;
or something more divine
than mother.

I began to look for
something else.
The world as presented to me
was wholly inadequate.
Mother said all my probing for
purpose would one day make her old;
or kill her before her time.

I tried desperately to fill the void
with something other than
Money
Fun
Relaxation
Mother.

As I got older,
I got curious about my father.
So cautiously,
I asked mom about him,
but her story never changed,

> *"Darling"*, she'd smile defiantly.
> *We're Zeus and Athena.*
> *Your precious brown body*
> *leapt from my brain the*
> *day I dreamt of you."*

She'd laugh and
tickle me with those
dainty,
smooth,
honey brown,
firm hands.

But that stopped being enough.

Then,
I left home for college
without even considering
in-state.

> *"Why work so hard*
> *when you don't have to?*
> *You'll regret this."*
> Mother said to me.

40

Her promises that
the outside world held
nothing but toil and stress,
and heartache,
didn't deter me.
My drive to escape my
inheritance yanked
more powerful than her
constant tug on me.

I'd earned a full scholarship,
so she couldn't torment
grandad, or blame him.

*"Don't you love me?
Think of what this
will do to us!"*

Despite her threat:

*"You won't get
a dime from us!"*

Grandad defied her;
he bought me a house
and filled it with furniture.

To mother,
happiness was freedom
from obligations.
The only things in life
worth doing
were the things you
absolutely wanted to.
And I absolutely wanted to work,
despite my Trust fund.

I found happiness to be
leaving a footprint in the world;
doing 'something' that mattered
for someone besides myself.
I needed to outlive my expectancy

Hence, I set off hoping
to find that 'something'
in education,
in a career,
but found it in someone.
It shone so brightly out of him
that I had to know about 'it',
before I cared to know him.
I would have bypassed
him altogether if I could,
but he knew Him.

I had never heard of 'God'
the way he spoke about Him.
I began to cram Him,
like pulling an all-nighter,
the night before an exam,
after blowing off an entire semester

My new God
infuriated mother.
She said religion was
A scam…
A farce.
She was terrified He would
replace her in my life;
but in God I found
something more than
a replacement for mother.

I found
Confirmation that
she was not ALL!

I found that
everything I believed
about being there for others,
putting others before myself,
having a reason to exist that

benefitted the world,
came from Him.

I learned that
He was the filler of
the void that had goaded me
since I was a child.

So,
mother's desire for
me to have nothing
but her left her with
nothing of me.

The night mother drowned,
grandad called to tell me.
They had been together
at the house by the lake.
She went out for a swim
and never returned.
I called him a liar.

Mother always warned me
that he was a liar.

"Never believe your
grandfather; he lies to make
us feel better, because he
wants us to forget the bad;
but it's always in us.
It bolsters us."

But then,
granddad wasn't telling me
something to make me feel better.
His words were suffocating.

"It's true, Sug."

Was all he said
over and over,
until I finally hung up the phone.

I hated him
for telling me that way.
He could have driven to me,
or convinced me to drive to him.
He could have
told one of his lies to
get me there.
Mother would have held me.
She would have cried with me,
told me how to feel,
what to wear,

45

and who to be.

He told me
She'd gone for a swim
in our lake in Upstate New York…
in March!!!
When she didn't return,
he went out to look for her,
and then called for help.
Her body had been recovered.

He made me promise
to get some sleep
before driving to the cabin.
Then the call ended.

I was left alone,
in my fancy little house,
empty;
wishing I had
stayed with mother
and gone with mother.
That's when the dreams started.

After the funeral,
I took a leave of absence from work
to help grandad amputate all the
loose ends that dangle after
someone you love dies.

It was then,
I found the newspaper clippings
about the woman who drowned
herself and her toddler son.
She'd driven right out
into the lake.
Our lake!

They were found,
seatbelts still fastened:
my grandmother and Uncle Leonard.

They were mother's clippings.
Buried deep in the treasure box
she'd kept since childhood.

The documentary
helped me to
understand the dreams:
their gene deafens.
Our gene drowns!

Maybe the answer to life for us
mimicked their cure?
Already a sinking feeling
pulled me down.
Maybe the spirit I'd tried to fill
with hope and peace
would succumb to it…
grandma,
mother,
me?

In the documentary,
the scientists' revelation felt
anti-climactic
and unbelievable.
What differentiated those relatives
that never lost their hearing?

"Simple, irrefutable belief!"

Those relatives that
remained hearing had never
believed they'd lose it
in the first place.

I had been looking for answers
to why my mother

48

and her mother before her
had drowned themselves;
to ensure that same desire
didn't end up engulfing me.

I have ridden
the wave of doubt,
that I'll probably end up
just like them.
And also stood on
an anchor of certainty,
there is no way I'll ever do it.
Though I know that
a flood may come,
I also know that
He can evaporate it.

*"My greatest fear
has always been
becoming mother".*

*"My only course is
to believe I will not
become my mother".*

THE SUMMER OF
THE 4 HUMILIATING
T-SHIRTS

It all started
with a trip to Disney
and a Star Wars themed T-shirt
that mom spotted, reading:

'TROOP LEADER'.

She squealed:

"That's ME!"

And totally disregarded the
individual allotment of $30
dad gave each of us for souvenirs,
arguing that 'clothing' didn't
fall under that category.
That shirt cost $36.

No use arguing;
we lived under a
'benevolent' dictatorship.
Besides, we were all impressed
that her argument worked.
Afterall mom lived under
a dictatorship that was
significantly less kind.

That was Spring break,
our last trip before dad
couldn't travel much anymore.
After that mom became obsessed
with Slogan shirts.
My eldest sister,
already a teenager then,
dubbed it:

'the Summer of 4 Humiliating T-Shirts'

We've called it that for 25 years now.

During the last week of school,
I overheard mom heaving
in weighted staccato that those
shirts were going to get her through
a hellacious summer...
- five kids

51

- one summer camp each
- VBS
- swim team
- CANCER.

She'd whispered that
last bullet point in a voice
I'd never heard from Mom before:
equal parts stormy and spooked,
together far exceeding 100%.
I peeked through the door then,
she sat on her bed,
her back to me,
I could feel the mass she bore.

Back then,
my siblings and I had
contradictory attitudes toward
one another, changing by the hour,
like weather man predictions.
A condition that often sank
our mother's heart.

She'd been an only child,
and her most powerful childhood memory
was countless hours of
kneeling by her bedside,

praying for siblings.
She'd birthed us
in a pattern of
girl, boy, boy, girl, boy,
and only stopped because:

"One more boy might kill me."

That summer we were
13, 11, 9, 7, 5
Jaiya, Jonah, Jackson, Jorah, Jett.

Although Jackson and I shared
a room,
friends,
interests, and
an immortal loyalty to mom,
it was Jaiya that I went to
with the cancer word.

Jaiya's admiration and loyalty
for mom pendulated in those days.
More often she pelted
disdain and disgust.
Mom had a
zero-tolerance policy for disrespect,
but Jaiya seemed to have been
offered immunity.

Instead mom caught her hurls
with firm gloves of grace.
She simply got looks of
utter disbelief,
understanding,
and pity.
The rest of us still received
death stares,
threats,
and privilege losses,
frequently.

As soon as the word
passed through my mouth
and Jaiya's face did not fall,
I knew she already knew.
We sat criss-cross applesauce,
knees barely touching,
in her walk-in closet,
where all the kid meetings were held.
She hadn't initiated one
in at least six months,
Jaiya was moving
further and further from
all of our sibling traditions.

It was there,

amidst clothes she
agonized over and mostly hated
that she told me it wasn't mom who
had cancer, it was dad.
And right there the burden
I'd tried to share with mom
Lifted.

Through the years I've
found it hard to forgive
myself for that leavening.
I've rationalized it:

> *"Mom was our primary care giver;*
> *she was the biggest influence*
> *in my life; she was near-perfect..."*

Still, I come out
shamefaced.

The next afternoon,
Jaiya called a kid meeting.
She was left in charge of us,
while mom and dad attended the
first of many appointments.
There among the dresses and skirts
that Jaiya and mom often struggled over,
we told the youngers;
and in those few hours,

55

we became "J5" again –
attentive
affectionate
united.
Grace filled our hearts,
we bickered less,
gave in more,
helped mom with the youngers.
Still, none of us could relate
to Jaiya's hatred of the T-shirts.

Of the four T-shirts,
Jaiya despised most the
one that read:

**'YA'LL GONNA MAKE ME
LOSE MY MIND.
UP IN HERE
UP IN HERE
-MOM'.**

Mom said it was based on
Lyrics to a rap song she used to
listen to as a teenager...

*"I never would have thought
back then that my own KIDS
could make me feel the way..."*

Then she beamed that
laugh usually reserved
for her girlfriends.
That laugh reverts her
face into her kid-self...
I loved that laugh.
That summer, that
laugh appeared frequently,
and she never reserved it again.

I never cared about
what my parents wore,
but I did find that shirt ironic.
Mom's mind was always
exactly where she wanted it.
She parented us
calmly
rationally
intelligently
annoyingly
clairvoyantly...
And I believed that if
anyone pushed her to
finally lose her composure,

57

it would be dad,
not us!

Dad left before daylight
and came home after dark,
six days a week.
He missed countless
-performances
-games
-dinners
-breakfasts
-family movie nights
-snuggle fests
-recitals
-pajama dance parties
-birthday celebrations.

He brought work home,
and he snapped at us,
and at mom over
-loud noises
-messes on the counter
-lost documents
-wasteful spending
-untidy rooms
-broken toys
-lights left on

-unflushed toilets…

Mom took his tyranny in stride,
she never shouted back.
She stood upright,
looked steely into his eyes
and silently absorbed his
accusations and dissatisfaction,
like a disinterested
Customer Service Representative,
who hangs up the telephone at
the end of the call and continues
her work without any effect.

Back then I couldn't understand
why she never stood up for herself,
or even for us.
Instead she constantly reminded us
that the life we lived:
-big house
-nice cars
-healthy food
-clean water
-devices
-sports opportunities
-recreational opportunities…
…everything

was due to dad's hard work.

We knew mom and dad had
loved one another long ago.
We'd heard the story,
they both loved to tell it:

They'd met in law school on
opposite sides of the debate team.
Dad had taken one look at her
and assumed that he would win,
because *"she was too beautiful"*
to be taken seriously.

For the benefit of my sisters,
he always adds:

> *"Of course, beautiful women
> are to be taken seriously and
> respected."*

Yes, they are equal, but
he mistakenly believed
that beautiful women
never had to work hard
and so they didn't.
But then, mom beat him
badly, so viciously that
by the end of the debate

60

he was speechless.
Dad is NEVER speechless.

From that moment,
he became obsessed with her,
and asked her out ten times
over thirteen months.
Her girlfriends told her
she'd sufficiently pounded
the conceit out of him; plus he's
tall, handsome, and athletic.

So, she finally agreed,
and they fell in love.
He became one of
the most sought-after
Litigators in the country,
and she became his wife.
Our mom.

With the shirt that read:

'YES, THEY ARE ALL MINE!
(AND YES, I DO HAVE MY HANDS FULL)'

Jaiya argued that mom
was being passive aggressive,

> *"which is hypocritical because*
> *you ALWAYS tell us not*
> *to be that way!"*

For the sake of sibling
harmony, I never told her
that she was only half right.
Mom always smiled her
'Fake-for-idiots-only' smile
and replied,

> *"Good measure,*
> *pressed down,*
> *shaken together,*
> *running over.*
> *My husband and I*
> *are so blessed!"*

Whenever someone
commented on her
hand to kid ratio.

But,
whenever someone,
inevitably elderly and white,
asked her if we were ALL hers,
she ALWAYS put them
in their place.

We lived in a part of town
where we were often
the only chestnut-skinned people...
in the library,
at the park,
in the store.
Mom took it as
a personal affront
the way white women could
prance around town
with multiple kids in tow
and no one ever batted an eye.

> *"Everyone takes one look at*
> *me with my tribe, and assumes*
> *I'm on welfare."*

Once an old white man
came upon her struggling
with the door at the book store,
she had the double stroller
and three of us on foot...

> *"Don't you think it's about time*
> *to stop having them?"*

He asked her,
instead of helping her
with the door.

Mom told the guy,

> *"The days of you and your kind*
> *controlling what happens to the*
> *progeny of my people are long over.*
> *You should be kissing our feet,*
> *since my attorney husband is*
> *gracious enough to pour his*
> *hard-earned money into your*
> *social security after your*
> *ancestors' atrocities.*
> *And God-forbid,*
> *your white privilege would*
> *ever stoop so low as to help a*
> *black woman open a door!"*

Then,
mom spit on his shoes!
On purpose!
The same mom that had
once marched onto the field
during a soccer game to tell
Jackson that she better not
see him EVER spit again.

Another time, a woman
asked mom how many
different fathers we had
right in front of all of us....

We all braced ourselves.
She responded to the woman,

> *"What is it about me that*
> *would cause you to presume*
> *that my four well-behaved,*
> *smartly dressed children,*
> *created by God Himself,*
> *would have more than one*
> *earthly father?"*

Her voice held so much
dignity that one couldn't feel
the full force of the daggers she
hurled until the very last word.
The woman stuttered,
red-faced in explanation,
as mom turned her back
and walked away.

We all followed her,
periodically glancing back at
the dumbfounded white lady.
Mom opens her mouth,
and people who assumed
they were better than her
shut up.

The fourth shirt read:

'MOMMIN' AIN'T EASY'

It was another
reference to her
teenage rap-loving days.
She wouldn't give any
further explanation.

The first time she wore it,
she'd just come down from
her shower, and was cutting
Water and Honey Dew Melons
for breakfast.
Jackson and I were
having a cardfight.
Dad swayed into the
kitchen from the Den,
where he'd been reading.

"It sure ain't!"

He'd chuckled
after glancing at her shirt.
He shook his head,
Jackson and I stopped our
game, mom froze.
He pulled open the fridge with

more strength than it
would have taken Jett,
grabbed one of the pre-made smoothies
that mom kept stocked for him,
and swayed back into the Den with it.
That was when I feared
that dad might actually die.

First,
he was adamant against
food consumption outside of the kitchen,
and he strictly followed
all the rules he imposed.
Secondly,
he'd actually acknowledged
that mom's job was hard.
Thirdly,
he'd taken time to read her shirt!

That summer,
dad stayed home more and more.
He lost too much weight
and his cocoa skin turned
an ashen grey.

At first,
we kids tiptoed and whispered.

We took extra care to
turn off lights
and flush toilets.
But the longer he stayed home,
the more comfortable we got.
We started being our normal selves.
Mom never changed.

All of a sudden,
dad started talking to us,
he asked us about our days,
and really listened to our answers,
asking follow-up questions.
He came to swim meets,
and our end of VBS party.

He started leaving home
after breakfast, and
making it back home
before dinner.
Then he started
working from home.
He laughed at Jackson's jokes,
he made jokes that even made Jaiya laugh.
He taught Jett to tie his shoes;
he painted Jorah's toenails;
he learned how to

cardfight with Jackson and I;
he started reading the same books as me,
and we discussed them.

The fifth shirt turned the tide.
Jaiya designed it herself.
Dad was at his weakest,
and so stayed home
most of the time.

Two weeks before Mom's birthday
he called us in,
one at a time,
so we could each pick out
a birthday gift for Mom online.

Jett chose a purse,
the strap on
mom's favorite one had snapped.
Jorah chose a purple necklace,
her favorite color was purple.
Jackson picked a dress,
even then he appreciated
a woman in a dress.

69

I picked out a book that she had
on hold on our library account.
I don't know how,
but dad talked Jaiya into
coming up with a "slogan"
to put on a Kelly Green shirt.

After mom opened it,
dad boasted that
it had only taken Jaiya about
a minute to come up with it:

> **'SUPER WIFE
> SUPER MOM
> SUPER HERO'**

Mom never played favorites,
she'd made it clear early that we
would not be treated the same.
She raised us according to
our individual needs.
If one person got a
bigger brownie than everyone else,
most likely, each one of us
would eventually get the
biggest brownie at some point.
But that day,

when she'd opened all of her gifts,
it was clear which item was her favorite.
Not only because Jaiya
had given an inch in her campaign
against the slogan shirts,
but also because dad had
memorialized that he could see
her work, and he appreciated it.

Dad went into remission
and never got cancer again;
but he didn't go back to
the way he was.

Every family has its myths.
Ours is that chemo and radiation
got rid of the cancer,
but mom was the one who
cured dad of everything else...

Miraculously,
she'd eradicated his
anger,
disinterest,
and once again,
convinced that ego of his
to Shut up!

My Brother, Laurence

We used to spread out across
the couches in the den,
Laurence and I,
after dinner and before showers.
He always got the longer couch;
we never talked,
the TV was on, always.
I'd be doing homework
or texting friends,
he would stare at the TV,
or out the window,
or at the wall.

Sometimes,

I'd stop and just look at him...
my brother, Laurence,
and think about how
I'd barely slipped into existence
despite his.

I was just six years old,
but already set into the role
of big sister the day I overheard mom
telling Auntie Via that she and dad
wouldn't have had me if they had
known what would happen to
my brother, Laurence.

> *That was before...*
> *I know she regrets those words*
> *Now.*

I've only ever known
my brother, Laurence
the way he was after the eclipse.
Mom says that he went
to bed one evening
a sun-kissed toddler,
blowing her kisses and
smilingly calling her,

> *"Mama"*

73

He woke up the next morning
as that toddler's shadow.

Laurence…
I say his name over
and over again at
night in my bed,
in the darkest part of night
when I'm alone, because
they couldn't bear to hear me,
and I don't ever want to
hear Mom scream again the
way she did the day he died…
over and over.

Laurence…
I loved him.
they loved him too,
but there was an entire
spectrum of feelings that
surrounded their love for him,
and most of them were bound up
by their love for me.
He would be my responsibility

eventually, and they dreaded that.

Once at the pediatrician with mom,
we happened to be waiting
with another family like ours.
Two boys sat on either
side of their dad,
they were about the same age
as Laurence and I.

The older boy
kept shouting out words
no one else
could have understood,
one at a time,
then silence,
and then a nonsense word,
then more silence,
and another nonsense word.

We all sat in the waiting room
as if no one heard it,
as if all six of us
were totally normal;
then the younger brother
got fed up,
he whispered at first,

but got louder and louder...

"Shut up!"

He was finally shouting.
The dad warned him quietly,
and looked at him sternly,
Repeatedly,

"But dad,
he's so embarrassing!"
The boy screamed.

I looked down at my feet,
then I said, as quietly as
I could, but loud enough
to be clear, with as
little judgment as possible,
which was very hard,
because of how much
I loved Laurence.

"My brother is just like yours.
He's quiet now, but sometimes,
he shouts out just like that.
And he likes to get up and
bolt for no reason at all;
just start running
no matter where we are,
and we have to chase him,

76

and sometimes hold him down,
which is almost impossible
for my mom and I.
Whenever I feel
like it's just too humiliating
I think about what it must
be like for him in a world
where everyone else is different.

I wonder if his normal self
is trapped in there,
watching, trying to get out;
or whether his normal self is
completely gone, and
all he is… is this person who
can't be like everyone else.
I don't know which one is worse,
but I know I'm the lucky one."

That younger brother
looked at Laurence,
who just sat there,
inscrutable
staring at nothing...
silent.
Then the boy looked at the floor
He didn't yell at his brother again

He looked ashamed and
his dad looked so defeated.
That wasn't what I'd wanted at all.
I just wanted
Both of them
to stop being angry.

Later,
mom told dad the story,
and he kissed my forehead
and said,

> *"What a blessing you are.*
> *How wise you are;*
> *we're the lucky ones.*
> *You're our Super-girl!"*

Their faces smiled,
but their eyes
had no gleam at all.
His nickname was Superman,
before his diagnosis, when
they were still overjoyed
by the news of me.
They nicknamed me.
My nickname stuck,
as nicknames do,
but his did not.
They are encumbered by guilt.

78

Still,
Laurence was gorgeous
You couldn't look at him
and see his autism.
He was my brother,
and even I could see
just how handsome he was...
'clothing line model' beautiful.
His chocolate brown skin
matched mine perfectly.
He was tall for his age,
almost six foot already,
and he was only fifteen.

His shoes were
already bigger than Dad's
He had hair that I envied...
'soft, tight spiral coils' that
dad kept really short
on the sides, with a
little bit of length at the top.
He had that teenage-boy body
that I shyly admired in other boys,
and I saw girls that couldn't tell,
eye Laurence.

Laurence usually

sat still for his haircuts.
Sometimes, I'd walk past
the bathroom, where
dad cut his hair and
I'd see Laurence there,
sitting on the wooden bar stool
in front of the mirror,
dad taking so much
care with the clippers.

I'd imagine them
talking about basketball,
or Laurence's latest crush;
and I'd think that I must have
the superpower of mind reading.

Catching dad's reflection in the
mirror, longing flared in his eyes,
as if I felt his yearning myself.

I did.
and I'd love to have a
big brother three years
ahead of me in school,
inviting his cute friends over
for me to faun over, and
getting annoyed with me for it.

Giving me advice on
crushes my own age.
Cheering me on
in volleyball, and
me cheering him on
in basketball,
or maybe soccer.
Fighting over the
last cinnamon roll
in the morning.

Him driving me
to school,
to volleyball,
to the movies,
to meet friends...
Me having to
tag along with him,
and keep his secrets
from mom and dad.
Him keeping mine.

Loving one another ferociously,
Liking one another too...
but sometimes,
pretending not to.

I was born two months after
Laurence was diagnosed.
We are 32 months apart.
Every milestone
I have ever achieved
has been a sad reminder
of something Laurence
either lost or would never do.

Even now…
especially now,
because until her dying day
mom would have
continued praying for a cure.
Mom called him the
'quicker Picker Upper'.
He could recognize all
his letters and knew most
of their sounds.
He knew his
numbers up to 13,
in English and Spanish.
He was potty trained
at 18 months,
which mom says was a blessing,

because that was one of the
things he never forgot.
There were other things
he never forgot,
or even perfected
after his diagnosis:
He could feed himself,
he could use a knife and fork
to cut his food, and
he knew what needed to be cut.

He could not bathe himself.
Mostly, he just sat and stared,
or paced and stared.
But when he ran,
he would take off
with no sense of danger,
in parking lots and across streets,
at church and in school,
with no warning at all beforehand.
His mind puzzled.

Sometimes,
he would walk up to us
and just stand there,
nearly belly to belly,
then we would hug him fiercely,

and he wouldn't fight us.
His arms would dangle at his sides,
stiff as a corpse, and
he'd stare off somewhere beyond;
but it was the only time
he'd allow true touch and
didn't fight us.
We stopped everything
each time he ended up
in front of us,
close like that.

He allowed me that
the day he died…
one last hug
right before we parted ways.

Laurence…
I say it over and over,
because I don't want it
to be bottled up inside me
and one day detonate.
We felt a lot of things
about Laurence,
but we were never angry
until he died.

The issue with Laurence was
that you just couldn't tell.
He was tall with an
athletic build.
A young, black boy.
People saw him with
whatever perceptions
they associated with
that description.

He just seemed so normal.
He didn't die for
who he was;
he died for who
they thought he was.
What someone his
size and color
represented to them.

All the sympathetic
airtime on CNN,
all the protesting about
how his life mattered.
All the witness testimony.
Our crumpled hearts...

none of it mattered,
because he seemed 'threatening',
based on all the information a
stranger with power processed
in assessing him for
less than a minute.

That afternoon,
mom had errands to run,
dad was working late,
my girlfriends and I wanted
to practice for volleyball tryouts.
Our favorite court was
within walking distance.
We always met at the school
and walked together.
Laurence had to come;
he tagged along a lot,
and no one ever minded.

My girlfriends always
helped me chase him down,
if he bolted.
And always hugged him,
when he let them;
teasing him that he knew
exactly what he was doing;

86

that he was the
smartest guy in town,
feigning obliviousness.

They were allowed to tease him;
they'd been my closest friends
since Elementary School.
They loved Laurence too.

The pavilion that
Laurence liked to sit at was
so close to the volleyball court
that we could run there in
seconds, if we needed to.

That day,
he had a red firetruck
in his hand that
he'd picked up on the
ground in the parking lot.
I hugged him fiercely-
thank God; before
he walked toward the
pavilion, and the rest
of us went to the court.

Between serves,

I glanced his way,
he sat, or stood and paced.
I noticed the police car pull up,
But didn't pay
much attention to it.
It stopped in
front of the pavilion.
Laurence stood and stared
off in a different direction,
something black in his hand now;
still, I did not worry.

Then the police officer
got out of the car; then
the volleyball walloped me
in the ear and I fell.
The girls ran over to me,
giggling and only half concerned.

Later,
they told me that
I whispered, "Laurence".
I don't remember that,
I remember my ears
ringing from the blow.

They followed my gaze,

we all saw the police officer,
gun drawn, shouting at
Laurence.
Then Laurence bolted
toward the playground,
the black thing still in his hand,
and the police officer shot him!
So many times…
Too many times…
And everyone screamed,
including Laurence.

He died right there
on the ground.

The police officers
held me back from him.
No one held him
as he died.

One of my friends called mom,
another called dad.
By then so many police officers
had arrived on the scene.
They held mom back
when she arrived, as her
first-born child lay face down

in a grassy patch adjacent
to a playground.

They held dad back
when he arrived.
His only son riddled with
bullets and exposed to
the elements.

I stood and stared at
my brother, Laurence,
who'd never said a
word to me, yet had,
managed to teach me
everything I know
about compassion,
about patience,
about unconditional love.

Mom screamed his name
over and over...
Dad held her and sobbed.
We didn't get to touch him
until much later in the morgue;
after the police interviews,
and the spokesperson said
my brother's death was:

"unfortunate!"

The black object
Laurence held was
a toy gun he'd found
under one of the tables
in the pavilion.

Later we learned that
a concerned mother had
spotted Laurence with the
gun and called 911.
She thought it might be a toy,
but the boy looked too old
to play with a toy gun...

"better safe than sorry."

I imagine her shrugging.

The police officer said
he instructed Laurence
to drop it several times;
but then he ran toward
small children and
the police officer felt
those children were in danger,
so, he shot Laurence

91

until he stopped running.

I imagine him shrugging too.
Now,
when I dream of Laurence
he's never himself,
he makes eye contact,
as he winks at me and
takes the last cinnamon roll.
He hugs me back,
squeezes me so tight
I wake up gasping for breath.

He whispers with dad
and they stop when I walk by,
both smiling mischievously.
He sneaks up behind
mom in the kitchen,
grabs her by the waist
and lifts her off the floor.
She's protesting fiercely
and also laughing.

All these things,
I miss about Laurence,
all these ways I feel gypped,
have nothing to do with

what I really lost when he died.
I lost a brother that I loved,
Sure.
But…
I would have been
responsible for him
for the rest of my life.
He might have affected every
major decision in my life,
from who or when to marry,
to when or if I'd ever
have kids of my own.

He was someone who
I might have to eventually
institutionalize.

When I'm being
completely honest,
I can admit silently in the
deepest dark of me that
I might be a bit relieved,
because someone killed
Laurence before I ever got the
chance to wish he were dead.

That there's nothing I truly

93

long for in the Laurence that
was only in the Laurence that
should have been.
I had truly loved Laurence
for exactly who he was
Yet, I wanted
so much more for us.

I wanted to know he
felt our love and
to love us in return.
No one had the right
to take away the hope
that one day he might.
But someone did.
And now we will
never know.

I pray...,
for my mother's sake,
that no cure happens
in her lifetime; I know
this is wrong.

But...,
how can she live with that?
With knowing that

Laurence could have
blown her kisses,
called her mama,
lifted her up in the air, and
been her sun-kissed boy
Again.

$$\pi = \$3.14$$

I spent lengthy hours
sitting cross-legged in
front of mom on an ugly,
burnt orange plush,
rectangular piece-a-carpet,
placed beneath me to
keep the grease from
smearing itself into her silky,
green-grey living room carpet.

That carpet had been purchased
with thousands of
Carmel Gooey cakes
and hundreds of

Pineapple Upside Down cakes.

Atop that old piece-a-carpet,
I watched television as
she braided or unbraided my hair
in predictable, linear cornrows;
something of a homemade abacus;
teaching me how
to add and to subtract.

To begin,
she'd gently turn my head
this way and that,
back and forth a few times,
drawing out the plans in her head
and then tell me how many plaits
she planned to do total.
After she'd complete each one,
I'd sing out how many were left.

> *"You have a brain*
> *for numbers, little girl.*
> *Someday you are going*
> *to go to high places with*
> *this head of yours"*

She'd jiggle my head gently
by whatever braid she was working on.

97

And she always bragged to dad
when he got home from work,

> *"Such a smart girl.*
> *Such a hard worker"*

Mom sold desserts from
home to neighbors,
co-workers of dad's,
friends of friends,
the church folks.
Our house smelled,
uninterruptedly,
as if everything in it
were coated in candy.

Mom must have decided
back then, when I first discovered
that if she announced she had
twenty braids to take down
and then finished two,
she only had eighteen left -
when I was only 4 years old
that I would be a mathematician.

When mom gets an idea in her head,
it remains there firmly planted,
No variables allowed.

So I grew up
getting straight 'A's in everything.
But the 'A's in mathematics
always held more value than
any others to Mom.

I didn't want to
be a mathematician
I wanted to be just like her:
buy eggs and sugar
and butter in bulk,
and then using a formula,
turn the dollops and granules
into goodies others would
pay to devour,
leaving them constantly
coming back for more.

To mom,
nothing mattered
more than an education,
except God.

I went to college,

knowing that mom and dad
had saved for my entire life
so that I wouldn't have to
struggle the way they
often had.

But all of those straight 'A's
had paid off.
All I really needed from them
was money for extras.
What I wanted from them was
money to open a little bakery.

I'd call it π = $3.14,
and hope she'd chuckle
at the mathematical reference.

I had only been on campus
for two weeks,
and was on my way to see a
Bike for sale when I walked by
a vacant store front for rent.
Peering into the
pristine glass door,
hands cupped on
either side of my face,
I knew that this was the place,

where my future could be made.

I continued on my way,
bought the bike,
and on my way back to the dorms,
rode by the place again.
The thought of opening it up,
nibbling at me,
I biked through campus,
drooling over the idea in classes,
wondering whether the
kitchen would be adequate.

I made friends,
and hung out,
but never studied,
and struggled with the classes
that should have come easy.

I received a warning letter,
putting me on academic probation
after the first quarter.

Then my grades at mid-year
were not good enough to
maintain my scholarship.
So, my parents had to

send me a check for
books and class registration.

There was no disappointment,
nor judgement in their voices.
They had the money,
it was intended for college;
I needed the money to stay there.
That was that.

I cashed that check and
called the building owner,
asking to see the little store.
I was told that it had
most recently been a
sandwich shop that failed.

Inside was a display case,
where I could put my desserts;
and a few round tables that
I could spruce up with
Flea market flips.
Then at the back was a
kitchen that mom could have
baked an empire in.

I put down first

and last month's rent,
and went out to buy a
Futon, Comforter,
and other items,
so I could sleep in the back room.

I cleaned out my dorm room,
and withdrew from school.

I was sure that by the time
my parents found out,
I'd be self-sufficient.
One day I'd be able
to pay them back.
Maybe even move them to me,
and let my mom help out sometimes.

I slept in the storeroom,
and in the morning,
set about getting the place
ready for opening,
which would have to
be in two weeks,
if I wanted to survive
on what money I had left.

Pies were my favorite dessert to eat

and mom had always told me,
halfway grudgingly,
that my talent for making pies
nearly matched
my mathematic ability.

"Near genius,
the way your crust waits
until it meets a tongue and
then melts, the way
your filling slides down
the throat, while the
taste buds beg it not to;
the way my resolve to
eat just one piece
always crumbles"

The day before
my Grand Opening,
while for the hundredth time,
I proofread the menu
before rushing it over to
the copy center to be
duplicated and laminated.

Someone knocked
urgently at the door.

104

I already had
my hand-stenciled wooden
'Come on In/Out Picking Apples'
Sign hanging there,
a small bell attached so that
I'd hear customers come in.

I placed the menu on
my work desk and
walked toward the door.
I saw her arm and
the rim on her hat
and immediately felt
a sugar rush...
Mom!

She bent down a bit,
to see around the sign in the door
and our eyes met.
I could feel my own shame
but not regret.
And I prepared myself to accept
that I'd likely be re-enrolled
by next week.
But I could not read her;
I couldn't tell if my shame
was a reflection of her...

disappointment?
Or her anger?

"Dad's parking the car"

She said to me,
giving me a tense hug,
and then pushing me
back a bit to take in the
little bakery, painted in
cotton candy pink,
honeydew melon green,
summer sky blue,
and a yellow so pale,
it reminded me of a
parasol I had as a young girl.
Ivory and gold accented
everything.

"Well, this is a wonder"

Was all she said,
Shaking her head.

By the time dad walked in,
grumbling about the
scarcity of parking spots
in college towns,
mom and I were already

seated at one of the tables,
sipping tea and nibbling the
cookies that I'd burnt a bit
before really getting to
know the ovens, but
hadn't yet thrown away.

I got up to receive his
gummy bear hug and to lock
the door I'd left unlocked for him.
And then I went to the back
to pour him milk and sugar,
with just a half cup of coffee

"Why did you do this thing?"
Mom asked, once we
were all settled at the table.

*"Because I got a whiff of it,
and the smell of it
got stuck there in my nose
and it had such a bite
that I started to taste it."*

"Why did you hide it from us?"
Finally, I could read her
face... I saw pain.

107

"Because all you ever saw
was me with numbers, and
I only ever saw myself as you"

Dad finally spoke up,

"You can't un-eat a chocolate cake.
Tomorrow we'll open and
find someplace for you to live,
because if we don't let you,
you might starve.
Mom will stay with you
as long as you need her;
you will re-enroll part-time,
and we'll help you
run this place full-time.

And one day when you're
working and studying,
and balancing books, and
cleaning, and trying to date
some love-sick boy, who
wants all of your time, you'll
wonder why you skipped the
part where you got to party,
and drank too much and
slept in; and just be a kid for
four more years."

108

Then Mom added,

> *"We never wanted you not*
> *to fulfill your dreams.*
> *All we wanted was for you*
> *to take your time growing up,*
> *and to fill your head with*
> *something to fall back on,*
> *just in case you were ever*
> *forced to wake up from*
> *those dreams."*

Now I wake up at 4:00 am
to start the day's cooking –
Muffins, Cookies, Cake,
Scones, and of course, Pie.
To boil the soup of the day,
and to make the list on
the chalkboard display menu
for the day's Sandwich options.

Mom gets there at 6:00 am
to start the displays.
Two employees come in at 6:30 am
to help with the morning rush.
We open at 7am
students, professors, and
Locals come in

for the specialty coffees
that are cheaper and better
tasting than the sludge the
chains sell.

I leave every morning at 8:30am
to make it to my 9am class.

At about 10:30am,
the second wave comes in;
the young mothers that meet
their similarly situated friends,
or come to use the Wi-Fi,
sip and snack
while all of their children
play several feet away
in the 'kidspace'
we added last year
when we bought the
entire building, and had
the wall knocked down.

I'm back in school fulltime,
I petitioned after a full year

of stellar grades and
I earned my scholarship back.

We bought a house and lived together,
and last month I bought my own house
Right down the street.
I can ride my bike to
the bakery every morning,
and to my classes from there.

Dad keeps the books,
files the taxes,
buys the supplies,
repairs and paints,
hires and fires.

Mom and I
cook, clean,
build relationships.

Even as prices increase
in restaurants all around us,
we still sell our jumbo slice of
Pie for $3.14.

The Architect

I am the master of
Remakes!
I see a glaring desire for
renovation, and
draw up the new image -
'just a fragment of the old',
in 30 seconds flat.

But then,
I have to persuade the owner.
Because despite her wanting
the blueprint to materialize;
despite her being dissatisfied
within the current framework,

She has to be
convinced that it's
possible and that the cost
is worth the expense.
That initial down payment
feels immense, but the
quality of my workmanship
conceives an end result that
is incomparable.

One might take me
for a sculptor
But, no,
I'm an architect.

My projects are often
dilapidated,
dejected...
I hone-in immediately
on the top three upgrades
if I could only get
my hands on her.

I note just how firm
and round the apse might be;
how I might reduce her veneer.
Give her a lengthened,

113

leaner appearance.

The frames strain under
the weight of emotions that
I will discover little by little
and shrink.

Shrink...
I'm an architect, yes,
but I play a convincing
psychiatrist as well.

I remove the insulation
from bodies and
stuff bereft souls with
accomplishment,
confidence,
beauty.

With enough hard work,
I design what she dreamt,
but could not 'DIY'.

The one was hunched over
timid; she had totally given up
Resigned to the fiction that
she would always shop

114

in the big lady section.
There was no mistaking
her beauty.
It arrested me.
Still, I envisioned her
brilliance shining from a
slighter neck and
upstanding shoulders.

It's been decades,
but I remember
becoming attached
to the excess, even as
I wished to erase it.
I recall being accustomed
to the way I'd acquired it.

I constructed the bridge
that marries desire and will,
I ran my way to the
other side and came out
muscular and lean.

I've been there,

115

So when
I'm done with them,
they'll never look,
even at cereal,
the same way again.

I walk up to her
in the cereal aisle
in the grocery store,
and introduce myself.
Looking directly into her eyes,
I tell her that I can help,
and I hand her my card:

Jarvis Wright
Cetified Personal Trainer
Certified Dietician
Wright Personal Training
WrightNOW Gyms, Inc.
EATwrightNOW Nutritional Coaching

My approach is Simple.
I'm never afraid to be direct.
I affirm that despite her beauty,
there is some work to be done,
and I'll be there every step
of the way holding her hand.

116

Of course,
those initial upgrades won't
complete the work.
But I work little by little,
and bill that way too.

I keep her too busy
and too exhausted
to keep up with
each expenditure.
So that by the time
the full invoice is received
She can look in the mirror
and say it was all worth it.
She'll happily pay the balance…
She would even pay more.
I like to think
I sculpt them back to
what God intended.

Now,
with this kind of arrangement,
inevitably, some find themselves
falling in love with me.
I know it's been a long time,
since someone who looks like me
has shown any interest in them,

117

truly cared for them,
really seen them,
encouraged them,
loved them.
I do, honestly tend to
love them all,
But I had never fallen.

In the end,
it's my job to
direct their gratitude
into loving themselves,
which always attracts
other men to them...
Better men than me for them.

It helps that
my gym is a community;
they each get to
see me with the others,
and then they see that
I'm the same with all;
that my love is totally
innocent of passion,
indicative only of
sincere care.

When my assistant
lists for me the names
of my new clients,
I hear hers and,
remember exactly
where I met her...
that cereal aisle.

I can see her lips,
the color of cinnamon,
her eyes are strangely round,
almost cartoonish,
but somehow working perfectly
on her heart-shaped face.
Her coffee bean skin is flawless
I'm startled at this
excitement at the prospect of
seeing her again, even after
weeks of not seeing her;
even though I spent less
than ten minutes with her;
Even though she's certainly
not my type.

I see her for the first time
in my gym in a long shirt
and sweatpants.

Baggy, to cover the imperfections.

I put her through all the
initial tests to assess her fitness.
I'm pleasantly surprised
she's strong.
She struggles through
my requests as if they are
already demands.
I tell her that
she's impressed me, and
her shoulders lift.

As always,
The down payment
must be discussed –
I give her the speech about
this time with me only
being worth 25%.
If she really wants to
get to her goal, she'll have to
work on her diet...the other 75%
of the battle.
Her shoulders revert back
and I realize that food is
her vice, not inactivity.

In addition to the monthly fee,
to join my gym and get
my instruction, she must
sacrifice the foods.
That's her down payment.

It varies for everyone -
Time,
Money,
Energy,
Hope,
Trust...
All the things one must
give in order to earn
what I'm selling.

There's always one thing
more precious than the others.

She signs up to come
see me three times a week,
to receive a customized meal plan,
to come to weekly weigh-ins.
She'll have unlimited access
to the equipment and classes.
Even her handwriting seduces.

"She's not my type!"

I remind myself twice
during our initial session.
I've never been this
distracted before during
an assessment.
I know this much
about myself –
I'm a recovering fixer,
instinctively attracted
to 'projects'.

In my youth,
I remodeled women
for myself and
felt fulfilled when
I made them better.
Only, that scenario
never works out long-term;
they never stayed mine long,
They flipped.

Now,
I consciously seek women
who are already
perfectly crafted,
who work hard,
who feel successful,

prioritize health,
who are a little bit vain.
Only that hasn't seemed
to work out either; not one
has been perfect for me.

It took months
for me to admit that
I look forward to seeing her;
her beauty cannot be upgraded,
even as she loses weight,
begins to stand erect,
starts wearing clothes that
accentuate instead of hide.
I see her differently,
as I get to know her.
Her beauty has breadth.

She reconstructs everything
I thought I knew about
my own taste.
She's not the one who
needs the overhaul,
but neither is she perfection.
She has a homemade
contentment.
Her laughter guts me

She's driven.
Her story demolishes
my ideal.

After spending
hours alone with her,
It's me that has been rebuilt.
I believe she is the one
The Creator handcrafted
specifically for me,
because those decades ago,
when I extracted the excess
from my own exterior,
I left the interior
untouched.
Over time,
I became a stiff relic,
good for nothing more
than looking at.

Then she remade me
I think about her when
I'm driving,
cooking,
working,
I catch myself still
smiling at something she said

about one of her students
five days ago.

She has expanded me;
spread me wide open.
I start working out with her
instead of coaching her.
We've shared about our
families…hers is far away
Careers…she's a college professor
Our faith…
mine constantly wavering,
hers rock solid and the
only reason she survived
Heartbreaks…
(her husband died two years ago)
We stay long after the gym closes;
eat Greek yogurt together in
the kitchen.

I don't worry that she's
confusing gratitude for affection.
I rationalize…
the best relationships
often start as friendships.
I feel guilty about charging
her; I stop looking at her

chart altogether.
Still, it feels like a violation.
I boldly instruct my billing
department to stop charging
her credit card.

A month later,
my assistant tells me...

> *"She called to inquire.*
> *"I didn't know what to tell her."*

I know her schedule,
of course, her next
training session is tomorrow.
I know I will not have
the nerve to tell her the
truth, facing her,
and I fail at fabricating a
plausible explanation.
So, I call her.

> *"Hello, it's Jarvis."*

My heart feels the way
it does after a fast run.

> *"Oh, Hey!"*

She sounds winded too.

> *"I just finished my*
> *thirty-minute cardio."*

126

"Without me?"

"Well, I wasn't sure if I'm still welcome. Your assistant was so cryptic. You're not firing me for lack of progress, are you? You told me this plateau was normal."

I can tell that she's teasing me.

"I keep telling you, the scale doesn't tell the whole story."

"So, are you giving me your services gratis, since I'm making WrightNOW look so good?"

she laughs then.

"Sort of. Actually, I am firing you…a little, or well, I hope to fire you."

"What?"

127

I can hear her uncertainty,
but she's smiling,
through her confusion.

> *"Well, I don't date my clients.*
> *Never have. Never will.*
> *I was hoping you'd consider*
> *my firing you as a kind of*
> *endearment…and then…"*

As badly as I fumbled
through that conversation,
She agreed!

> *"But, only if I can*
> *still use the gym."*

To which, I respond that
she cannot…at least for
a while; for the sake of
the other clients.

One year later...
we run together,
bike together,

and cook together.
Sometimes she comes
after the gym closes...
eating Greek yogurt
in the kitchen after closing
became our thing.

When she finally comes
back to the gym,
it's no surprise to anyone;
they all knew,
like one of those signs...

'Closed for Remodeling'
Had been tattooed
on my forehead.

THE
MARATHON

I reach out to halt the
alarm's hushed chime
even before it sounds.
It's on the lowest volume,
yet my heart won't let it
ring for my morning runs.
It knows to jolt me
ahead of the clock.

I must wake up
while the rest of the
house lay dormant
for a little while…
before I have to wake the

children and fix their breakfasts,
bag their lunches, put two
on the bus 7:37am, and
drive the others in at
8:15am and 9:00am.
Before I have to hear,

> *I don't like that!*
> *Not fair; she's wearing*
> *my shirt!*
> *Stop looking at me!*
> *He ate the last one!*
> *Why do I have to wear that?*

My reflective running gear
is already laid out,
every second counts,
getting dressed,
brushing my teeth,
tip toeing down the stairs…
All done under my breath
in the dark.

To stir anyone would mean
a missed opportunity, and
Lord knows, I've had
enough of those.

Out on the front porch,
door closed unflinchingly
behind me, I tie my shoes,
set my watch to run,
and take off.

The sky is in that middle place
between dark and relief,
I always feel safer in
five minutes or so, when the
flashing lights on my shoes
aren't quite necessary anymore,
but stopping to click them off
would make my overall pace
read inaccurate.

So, uselessly, they flash
through the entire run.
It's this first mile that feels
the most uncomfortable;
when the only thing I'm
running after is my breath,
when my legs aren't quite
convinced they can do this.
After that first mile,
my effort merges with my
entire being with such fluidity.

The middle miles are the
reason I run, it's here,
as the dark gives way to a
glow so magical and measured
that I miss it every time,
even as I witness it.
That I talk to God; I give thanks
for every muscle that allows me
to be out here running.
I ask for forgiveness for
the times I have not been
the blameless child that
He created me to be.
I pray for everyone I love,
for everyone I know,
and even those I don't,
but have heard about.
   Every Fear
     Failure
       Obstacle
gets crushed by the weight
of His majesty; He turns all
of it into Courage
     Perseverance
       Advantage
He directs my footfalls in a
way that I could not have

133

imagined years ago.
He blessed me with running,
and with every mile I log
I grow closer to who I should be.
I am evidence that
miracles do happen...

I. Run. Marathons!!!

Thinking back now,
I marvel...
Running was never
something I did
or thought I could ever do –
unless I was being chased
by something bigger than me.

A mother of four...
Four kids in seven years,
overweight for most of my life;
never been an athlete.
I always preferred
reading,
quilting,
cooking,

Raising kids.
Always on my feet, but nothing
that increased my heart rate,
and nothing that made me sweat.

Until I saw that 'something',
bigger than myself,
after that fourth child,
when I looked in the mirror,
Naked, and thought

What in the world?!

Because the woman
that glowered back at me
was massive and fluffy
and unhealthy.

Discontent had chased me
and finally caught up.

That day, I downloaded a
'Couch to 5k' App.
The name alone was irksome,
because I was not an athlete,
but I had never been a
couch potato.

I ran the 5k

Then I downloaded
the 5k to 10k App
and ran the 10k.
Then I joined a Run Club,
and started running with
other people who loved to run.
We ran races together, and
they became my closest friends;
we became a family.

We talked kids
and housework.
We talked husbands
and dreams
and books
and politics.
We agreed
We disagreed
We considered
Respected
Loved.

Running is not a team sport,
you can do it alone.
You don't have to
rely on anyone else.
But there's something

about being a team,
about doing it with someone
you're close to; even if you're
at mile 8 and they're way up
ahead, you're connected.
You experience it together
and trade stories, and have
them forever.

I never got skinny, but I
shrunk and my muscles toned,
hard in all the right places, but
still soft in the places that my
kids liked to snuggle up against,
and my husband appreciated.
I like seeing myself naked
in the mirror.

I trained with my friends
often and by myself,
with God, more often.
We decided to run a half
marathon… we ran several.
And because there was no
other place to go but farther,
we signed up for a marathon.

The marathon
beckoned as the definer.
We called ourselves runners.
Yet, there was one distance
that eluded all of us.

Doubtful…
each of us bolstered
by the others' faith.
Each of us secretly
hoping the other would
back out first.
No one did.
So, we ran the marathon,
and it was horrible.
Then we signed up
for yet another one…

Though I'd said,

                "Never again!"

after the first time,
when my phone died
at mile 22, and took my
music with it.
Then my watch died

and with it, my GPS.
Lost…
Where was I exactly?
By then, every .1 mile mattered.
By then, the mile markers
had been taken.
The paper cups at the
abandoned aid tables were
all overturned,
their water dripping from
cup to table, to course.
Stomped on and evaporating,
much like my resolve.
Crossing the finish line
within the 5.5 hour time limit
seemed a far-off mirage.
Would I DNF?
-(Did Not Finish)

No matter…
I'd grab the SWAG.
They will give me
the BLING.
Beg,
Borrow,
or Steal,
I'd earned It.

By now,
every single step was a misery.
Like walking barefoot on a
path of electrified needles.
I was sure that everyone
who had run a marathon
and encouraged me in it
HATED me!
All of them...and I didn't
like them very much either.
I would tell them that, if
I survived; because the
first person that ever ran
a marathon DIED.

How had I taken that
fact so lightly before?
But, I had to survive.
For the children.

Still, I'd be different
I would tell the truth to anyone
who said they were thinking of it
I could not, in good conscience,
recommend running a marathon.
Because marathons

are so deceptive;
their strike so swift.

Just a few miles ago,
I had been in such a pleasure.
Like an eagle
soaring near heaven.
My feet
barely touching the ground
The wind
beneath my wings
The sun
illuminating my strength
and infinite energy.
My playlist
specifically composed to give
a bounding rhythm to my gait.

I remember thinking at mile 10,
I've definitely got 16 more in me!
And then at mile 17,
less than 10 more!
But somewhere after mile 22.
Maybe 22.15?
I slammed… toes first
into an impenetrable Wall.
I'd heard about it, of course.

I'd done all the research and
talked to the veterans, remember.
But it's like when you're
told that you won't sleep after
having the baby…EVER.
Until you experience it yourself,
you really cannot imagine
the veracity.

The Wall they talk about is
not hyperbole; and just a
split second later, I can't go on.
When there were only 4 more miles,
when I had already run 22 plus.
Every time I decided to walk,
I thought about the time limit,
and the SWAG
and the BLING
and I kept running
until I couldn't.

Then up ahead I spotted someone
wearing the same shirt as me
and thought…

> *'out of body experience…*
> *NOT good.'*

Then I remembered,

142

it must be Bere.
She had driven Shelly and I,
and walked us to the start
and hugged us both good luck.
We all wore our royal blue
Y Run Club shirts –
'Kindred Soles, Diverse Goals'.

She had been waiting
the entire time… 5 hours?
She sprung to me and when
she did, I realized that what
I was doing with my legs
was no longer running, and
couldn't even be considered jogging.
She ran beside me.
I tried to match my amble
with her agile canter,
but failed.

Her words of encouragement
an elixir to my downtrodden soul,
and balm to my inflamed soles.
The cement surged to pound
into them, step by excruciating step.
I told Bere I could not go on,
but kept "running?"

Or toddling to the finish, finally!
To Shelly, and muttered
                    "I'm so sorry..., I'm so sorry"
into her ear, as we hugged.
Because it had been my
bright idea to run a marathon.

Shelly had no idea what
I was muttering
Gibberish?
Was I speaking gibberish,
or was she hearing gibberish.
Because we were both delirious
with pain,
with pride,
in disbelief that a marathon
could be so brutal, and
that we had both endured.

We both limped back to
the car and fell asleep on
the ride home.

That night
I went trick-or-treating
with my family, because
a little thing like a marathon

never stopped a mother.

The next day
Shelly and I chatted on
the phone, both laid up with
DOMS,
  -(Delayed onset muscle soreness)
watching the New York
Marathon, marveling at the
strength of those athletes,
deciding to forever leave
marathons to them.

But then,
Bere got the idea to run
one the next year for her
40th birthday in Charleston.
A Girls' Trip!
We all laughed about how
only a group of moms would
decide to run a marathon
as a 'getaway.'
And I asked Bere,

"You were there, right?
When we could hardly
walk afterwards?
When we nearly didn't make it?

145

When we fell into comas
on the car ride home?"

Nevertheless,
Bere registered.
I appealed to Shelly that
marathons are savage!
Remember the DOMS???
Still, Shelly registered.
And I told them,

"I will play Bere for this episode,
I'll be happy to drive,
encourage, and celebrate with
you afterwards"

They just laughed,
because they knew
FOMO
    -(Fear of missing out)
Then I registered,
with the same denial I
embraced on the decision
to have each of my three
subsequent children, even
after the one before was
so agonizing...

"Maybe it won't be as bad
this time..."

146

A steadfast focus on the
end result.

So, it was time to train.
The guarantee -
that ritual of increasing my
long run mileage, gradually
until I reached 20 miles.
This, yet another ruse of
the veteran marathoners.

They tell the amateurs that
once you get to 20 in your
training, you can rest assured,
definitely run the marathon.
If you can run 20, you'll be fine
for the last 10k, rest assured,
on momentum
on adrenalin
on… the logic varies,
but it's the same idea:
To HIDE the fact that anyone
with training, can run 20 miles.

But everyone,
*(except those super humans you
see on television running sub*

4 minute miles the entire course),
shuts down somewhere
shortly after mile 22.
And if you allow yourself to
experience that before
marathon day, you'd never
run it; you'd give up.

So, you get to 20,
then you're rest assured.
Bere got to 20, and decided
to run a 22... and she did!
Yet, she worried about the
marathon; and Shelly also
did her 20, but I never did.
I hadn't even found
consistent time on the *dreadmill*.

I was truly perplexed.
Why couldn't I get the miles in?
But I DO have four children.
So, for one reason or another
my long runs got postponed
over and over, until a week before
Charleston Marathon Day,
when I should have been on my taper,
I had only run as far as 13 miles,

and even that 13 was only once
13 out of 20 – 65%!
Is that a D or an F?
It will be fine.
I will be fine.
Once I got to packet pick-up,
I'd just drop down to the
easier half-brother.
No big deal.
I hadn't REALLY wanted to
run another marathon anyway.

So, I obsessed for a week
I texted Frannie and Karen,
they were coming along
as the drivers,
encouragers,
and cheerleaders that I was
supposed to be.

They did not plan to run -
Frannie was injured
and Karen had made It clear
since we first became running
friends, she would never
run a marathon...Ever!
They were coming to be Sherpas.

149

They both advised me to
drop down... I hadn't trained,
I didn't want to risk injury.
Bere and Shelly would understand.

But ultimately, Shelly
convinced me to do it.

> *"You'd regret it"*
> She'd said.

And anyway,
I'm always telling my kids
to follow through with their
goals... Never give up!
So I stuck with the marathon,
and prayed the entire night before.
How could I sleep?

> *"God, please get me to mile 20*
> *If you get me there,*
> *I can walk the other 6.2*
> *Please Lord, let me run and*
> *not grow weary, until mile 20.*
> *Help me walk and not faint*
> *for the remaining 6.2"*

I also tell my kids to pray
about everything.
For this race the time limit

was 6.5 hours.
So I knew if I ran 20 at a
steady pace, I could walk 6.2
and still get done in time.

Karen and Frannie
walked us all to the start,
encouraged us,
hugged us good luck,
told us at which miles
they'd meet up with us;
check on us,
hold up signs,
cheer us on,
See what we needed.

We took off
Shelly in the lead, as always
a PR in mind.
   - *(Personal Record)*
Me in the middle,
because I knew I needed
to make good time early on,
then Bere.

Again,
The run became

a glorious illusion.
I hadn't run much
and I truly love running
I could run with reckless
abandon for hours,
Music
conducting my foot strikes.
Wind
beneath my wings.
Trees, streets, people, cars
and houses in my periphery.
And for the first time
since I registered,
I was not nervous.
I would have my time
with God.

So I ran
And ran
And ran.
I talked and laughed
with other runners
as I passed them,
or they passed me.
And this is one of many
reasons why running thrills me.
Runners are some of the

most positive people in the world.
I had no second thoughts
as the halfers split away.
I looked forward
to seeing Shelly and Bere
at the turnarounds.

I looked forward
to what the signs
Karen made would say.
She is the ace of positivity
and encouragement.
I looked forward
to Frannie saying,
or doing something
unforgettably hilarious.
I held no expectations at all,
but hope for the promises
of pride,
of that high I get.

At mile 12
I took a picture on the pier,
and quickly posted it on FB.
At mile 17 I chatted with
my third child, because
I'd made the mistake of

telling the children,
laden with the guilt of
leaving them, they could
call me any time.

When I came upon
Frannie and Karen
At mile 17.8
*(By then my feet had
a negligible ache)*
Frannie sat on the curb,
took off her shoes, and
offered me her socks.
When I said

"No thanks"

She offered them to a
Stranger running by.
I hugged Frannie and Karen,
I took their picture, holding
the signs to post on FB later.
To have as a keepsake.

And then it struck again!

The next time I saw Frannie,
Mile 19? 20?
She said she'd gone to

154

get Bere water.
Karen was with Bere.
Was it really just 3 miles later?
But that's how the Wall works.
An emissary of velocity.
One minute, you're rejoicing
in freedom, the next smashing,
feet first, into brick.
I had to walk.
I was convinced my feet,
in tender, pinching agony,
were bleeding.
My left ankle felt as though
it was made of glass.

The pavement,
an unrelenting hammer.
Bere was not far behind,
so Frannie went to her
with the water.
There was no doubt they'd
catch up to me,
Bere was still running.
Minutes later, they did
catch up... Bere and Frannie.

Injured Frannie kept running

to the finish line.
Karen stayed to walk with me
every single reluctant mile,
carrying a backpack of supplies –
Body glide,
Nutrition,
Hydration…
We talked
and we laughed,
and I told her
NEVER again!

I limp-ran across the finish line
within the time limit
Again, with a friend,
so much more than
just a friend… Kindred Soles!
And, of course, with God.

He answered exactly what
I had asked.
I had run the 20
and walked the 6.2.
So next time I'll pray
He helps me carve out
the time to train…
some with Him

and some with them.
And that He takes me all
the way to the finish line…
Running.

But for now I'm content
trading stories and giving
my testimony about how
great it feels to be in
the small 0.5% that can say

"I Ran 26.2!
…twice so far,
and still counting…"

Yes, I did say NEXT TIME!
I will run the marathon again.
But, this time I will train
and be ready for the race.
I won't go out again like that –
Limping through the last 6.2 miles.
No!

The next time I face
The Marathon,
I will finish strong!

The Notes They Played

The Notes They Played

CPSIA information can be obtained
at www.ICGtesting.com
Printed in the USA
LVOW11s1500141217
559732LV00001B/3/P